RockStar

DENTAL ASSISTANT

*Follow me on my journey and
learn how to get more appreciation,
respect, and satisfaction*

TIJA HUNTER, CDA

INDIE BOOKS
INTERNATIONAL

Additional Copyrights and Trademark References:
MARY KAY® is a registered trademark of Mary Kay, Inc.

ISBN-10: 1-947480-58-8
ISBN-13: 978-1-947480-58-2
Library of Congress Control Number: 2019905443

Designed by Joni McPherson, McPherson Graphics

INDIE BOOKS INTERNATIONAL, LLC
2424 VISTA WAY, SUITE 316
OCEANSIDE, CA 92054

www.indiebooksintl.com

TABLE OF CONTENTS

CHAPTER 1

Why You Should Become a Rock Star Dental Assistant

Don't compare yourself to anyone.

You are uniquely you, and you are wonderful.

You are invited: *Take the journey to become a rock star dental assistant who gets more appreciation, respect, and satisfaction.*

Growing up, I remember my mom telling me, "I don't want you hanging around that group; they will ruin your reputation." In junior high school, I don't think I even knew what that was. What was a reputation? How could I ruin something I knew nothing about?

She went on to say that hanging around with bad people gave me a bad reputation. You truly are a reflection of the company you keep.

One of my favorite memoirs was written by Yvonne Thornton: *The Ditch Diggers' Daughters*.[1] I stumbled on this little gem when the movie version was playing late one night. The film was so powerful I had to get the book. In it, Yvonne's father is bent on his daughters succeeding; he dedicates his life to seeing that cause to its fruition. Although sometimes his family didn't agree with his tactics, his heart was in the right place.

In one scene in the film version of the story, he drives his family to a very poor section of town and sits in the car with them. He tells his girls to look around them. See the people? The way they are dressed, the cluttered streets, the trash, their attitudes, the looks on the faces? Frowns, not smiles? "Do you want to live like this," he asks. "Do you want more out of life?"

---

[1] Thornton, Yvonne S., and Jo Coudert. The Ditchdigger's Daughters: A Black Family's Astonishing Success Story. New York: Kensington, 2002.

In the next scene, he drives them uptown to a nice part of town. Now he asks them if they want to live like these people. The streets are clean. The freshly dressed people have smiles on their faces. "Do you want to dress like them?" His point is, if you want the best, hang around the best. Be your best. You are a product of the company you keep, so surround yourself with people who support you, encourage you, and elevate you.

I know firsthand how being with the wrong person can hold you back, keep you from realizing your potential, and prevent you from seeing your worth. Take care of yourself first and foremost; it's the best thing you can do.

So before we go any farther, let me offer the most *basic* advice.

As a mom, I always thought that I needed to take care of my kids first. There was no time for *me*. I had to take care of them, give them all I had. As they grew older and moved on with their own lives, I realized that I had neglected myself. Then taking care of me became a priority. Please take a lesson from my experience; *you* are the greatest asset you have. If you have children, the best thing you can do is to take care of yourself *for them*. Don't put yourself second, because *they need you*. You need yourself to be your best for them and you.

When you are traveling on a commercial flight, you'll notice flight attendants tell you the safety features and what to do if the oxygen mask should fall from the overhead compartment. They always tell you, "If you are traveling with a small child, please place the mask on yourself first and then help the child with theirs." Put simply, if you aren't strong and healthy, you can't help anyone else.

It seems women have a tendency to do that: put ourselves last. If I had to go back and tell my younger self anything, it would be to take better care of my skin, use moisturizer on a daily basis, eat better, walk more, and buy the best shoes I could afford. When you are younger, if you are like me, you just don't think about these things. I was invincible when I was younger. But as you age? *Ah.* That's when you realize all of the things you should have done differently.

Buy the good shoes. Your feet align your entire body; your spine, your hips, and your knees. If you don't have support in your feet, over time, your body takes a beating. Back in the day (the 1980s) it was customary for dental assistants to wear white pants and shoes, and I bought inexpensive white canvas shoes because I could throw them in the washer with some bleach and they would emerge looking new again. And when I couldn't wash them anymore, I threw them away because they were so inexpensive. Years later, I found out how bad that was for me. Your feet need support. Also, just because shoes are expensive, that doesn't mean they are supportive. Purchase a good pair of shoes and save them only for work. They will last you longer, and your older body will thank you for it later. You can replace your knees, your hips, just about everything else; you can't replace your feet.

Keep moving. I remember one of my first bosses used to talk about his parents, who were very active in their seventies. They had camped from one end of the country to the other and loved to travel. We had patients about the same age as my boss's parents, yet I couldn't imagine this couple traveling and being as active as my boss's parents. My boss used to say, "You have to keep moving. Never stop." I didn't think much about that then; I was in my twenties and invincible. Now that I am older, I realize what he meant. Sitting for long periods of time is hard on an older body. You must keep moving. Exercise didn't seem necessary when I was younger. After all, I was chasing two boys. Now, it's essential that I keep moving and working these old muscles. Not moving will age you fast.

Never stop learning. School was not easy for me. I really just went so I could visit with my friends. I hated speaking in front of people, and yet many classes required me to get up and give presentations. I stressed over it; I would lie and say I was sick on any given day we had to present our work in front of the class, in hopes of getting out of the assignment. I hated homework and rarely did it, only completing assignments when absolutely necessary.

Isn't it funny that something you once thought you hated can become something you love?

Learning, presenting, researching and writing are now things I dearly love doing. I wouldn't want my life any other way, yet I fought them for so long.

The dental assisting profession is ever changing and growing. The changes I have seen in thirty-seven years are crazy—incredible. So, staying on top of those changes is absolutely necessary if you want to be successful. No matter where you are, or what profession you are in, educating yourself is a priority.

I've had dental assistants tell me, "My doctor won't send me to that seminar." Or, "My doctor pays for the seminar, but not my wages while I'm there." I'm no expert in human resources, so I can't give advice on specific cases, but I will say *don't wait for your doctor to send you.* If your doctor pays for the course, but not your wages while there, *go.* Soak in all you can. Remember, the knowledge you gain will always stay with you. It doesn't belong to the practice or the doctor. Once you've absorbed it, that knowledge is yours.

With so many websites offering free education, there is no reason to not be educated. Whether you attended a yearlong program, a twelve-week program, or even trained on the job, it doesn't really matter. What matters is the education you have undertaken since the first day of your dental assisting career. What have you done to grow? What have you done to expand your knowledge? What are you waiting for?

Back in the early days, I heard about this exam you could take to become a Certified Dental Assistant (CDA) through the Dental Assistant National Board (DANB). I also heard, "You don't need that to get a job," "You know that won't get you any more money," and "Why would you do that when you don't need it here?" And I listened. At the time, I would just agree and move on. I was allowing other people to dictate my career. I was listening to their insecurities and took them up as mine.

Never allow anyone to dictate your future. They aren't you. They don't walk your path. Their dreams aren't your dreams. Their motivation isn't your motivation. Don't listen to anyone who says, "You don't," or "You can't." Do things for you. Do something because you want it, not because someone else says you need it. I didn't take that CDA exam until I was in my twenty-ninth year as an assistant—and it was the best decision ever. Practicing for that exam ignited a desire in me to learn and grow. It made me realize just how much I loved learning.

With education comes confidence. The more you learn, the better you become. Not just in your career, but in everything you do. Because that confidence will radiate through your life.

TIJA'S TIDBIT

"A flower does not think about competing with the flower next to it. It just blooms."

SENSEI OGUI, ZEN SHIN TALKS

You are special in your own way. Be you.

CHAPTER 2

My Mess-To-Success Story

I was shy growing up. I didn't like to talk to people, and I hated to talk in front of people (imagine that!). My mother and stepfather had a tumultuous relationship, and I believe that played into my shyness—I was afraid to speak out. My brother, on the other hand, has always been the funny one. I remember listening to him growing up and thinking, "I wish I could make people laugh the way he does." He was always so quick-witted and knew so much. I envied him. To this day he is the exact same way he was growing up; funny, knowledgeable, can eat anyone under the table and is still the skinny one.

I believe my shyness prevented me from seeing my potential. I was afraid from an early age. I was afraid of failing, afraid of trying because I might fail, and afraid to reach out. I didn't feel smart, and I was intimidated by the "smart kids." Even though I was friends with them, I was shyer around them. I was always the peacemaker, I didn't want anyone fighting, and I did my best to smooth conflict so it didn't escalate. I was even the caretaker at school, and I remember consoling a classmate in third grade who was being bullied by a boy. I did anything to prevent conflict; later I would find out just how far I was willing to go.

I grew up with my mother, stepfather, and brother. My biological father wasn't in the picture. I have vivid memories of dreaming of him. What was he like? Would he love me? Did I look like him? As I grew up, I wondered how he would have been there for me. How would he have helped me? How would my life have been different with him in it? Sadly, I met my father for the first time at his funeral when I was thirteen years old. In a way, I got to create the dad that I wanted.

But I always felt rejected by him. Why didn't he want to meet me? Was there something wrong with me? Why didn't he want me? This is an unnecessary burden that most kids raised in the absence of a biological parent place on themselves. I felt rejected, and of course, that added to my shyness; it kept me an introvert throughout my school years.

I was devastated at losing a man that I had built up in mind. He was my knight; he was my protector; he was my dad. There were many stories of what a great man he was, and many of his dark side as well. Each of us has a story to tell. It's the story of us; the good, the bad and the ugly.

I believe I had many reasons at that age to sink inside myself and not grow. I don't feel I was encouraged, empowered, or supported. My family, like many others, had its own issues. We were poor, we moved a lot, and it was clear my stepfather and my mother didn't get along very well.

I grew up in several small towns in Illinois. I never really knew why we moved around so much, but I truly hated it. Before I attended school, we lived in several towns, from Chicago to Staunton to Pittsfield; we seemed to roam all over the place. My family came from Pike County, Illinois, so that always seemed like "home base" for me.

We were poor, and I don't think I realized just *how* poor we were. Looking back, it's easy to see, but at the time, it was just life. We made the best of it because as kids, we really had no idea; we enjoyed growing up in the 1960s.

I attended kindergarten in Granite City, Illinois, a suburb of St. Louis where my parents had jobs. We lived in a trailer home not far from my mom's workplace. I remember walking to school every day with my older brother. Isn't it funny how you remember some precious moments like it was just yesterday?

From there, we moved again, and I attended another school from first to sixth grade in Mitchell, Illinois, living in three different homes. This was really the base for my childhood and where I have some very fond memories. Each time we moved my heart would ache. By the time we got to the third home, it was out-of-district for us. So in my seventh-grade year we attended a different school in Roxana, Illinois.

I remember day one of that year as if it were yesterday. As you can imagine, my name isn't the easiest to pronounce. I get called all kinds of names. That morning, standing at the bus stop with kids I did not know, going to a school I knew nothing about, and trying to introduce myself was embarrassing. I was so shy, and they just kept asking, "What? *What* is her name?" When all of your classmates are Mary, and Tammy, and Bobbie, being the standout isn't a good thing.

By the end of that year, my parents were on the road again, taking us just thirty minutes away, but out-of-district one more time. The

first day of school in my eighth-grade year,
I cried as I got ready, and my brother and I
begged to go back to our previous school,
the one we had just gotten to know, where
we had *just* made friends. My mom drove
us down and signed us up at our previous
school. By the end of that year, my mom had
found a place to live in the district we wanted,
and we moved closer to school. This time, we
would be moving *without* our stepfather, and
thus a new journey began for us. I was able to
stay in that school until I graduated from high
school. Wherever I go, Roxana will always be
my home. Once a Shell, *always* a Shell!

After high school, I was engaged to my
sweetheart, and shortly after that, I realized
I was pregnant. Our marriage was short
and full of anger with no communication.
We separated when our son was just seven
months old. At the ripe old age of nineteen,
I was divorced with a seven-month-old baby
boy. I had no direction in my life. Because of
moving so much as a child, I wanted stability.

I created, in my head, my dream life. What I had thought was going to happen (the comfy home and the white picket fence) had just come to an abrupt halt, and I had no idea where to go from there. I can't remember a lot of advice that my mother gave me, if any, but I do remember lying on her couch shortly after my high-school sweetheart leaving me, feeling completely sorry for myself, drowning in self-pity, and my mother looking at me saying, "The sun is going to come out tomorrow, and the next day, and the next. You can't just lie around waiting for something to happen, because life goes on." I remember that moment well because as soon as she said it, I knew she was right. I knew I needed to take the ball.

That was the last time I ever felt sorry for myself.

I was young, I had a beautiful baby boy, and I needed to get up and be there for him. It was the lowest point of my life. I had no idea how to provide for my son. I had to sign up for food stamps and assistance; it was at the office where I did so that I was given the name of a government program that helped unemployed people go through school. Back then, it was called the Manpower Development and Training Act; it has gone through several different incarnations since and is now referred to as the Workforce Innovation and Opportunity Act.

Three months after my divorce, I took a series of tests to evaluate my strengths and weaknesses, and from there, the agency coordinating the program recommended five areas they felt I would be best suited for as a profession. Although I don't remember what four of them were, one area stood out to me: *dental assistant*.

I'd had braces in junior high, and I loved my dentist and his assistant. As I looked at the list, the choice was clear. "Dental assistant," I said. Within two months, I was accepted into the program at a local dental assisting school and began studying just one week after my son's first birthday. Looking back, I'd say it was one of the best decisions of my life.

It seems all through my young years that just as I got into a comfort zone, I was being ripped out of it to a new life. Maybe that was preparation for my life to come: Getting out of my comfort zone in order to grow and become who I am today.

TIJA'S TIDBITS

"If your ship doesn't come in, go out and meet it."

JONATHAN WINTERS

Don't wait for something to happen; make it happen.

CHAPTER 3

My Faith Was The Glue That Kept Everything Together

My parents—my mother and stepfather—
like most who grew up during World War
II, attended church. I do not remember my
stepfather talking much about his relationship
with a church. My mother, however, was very
vocal about churchgoing. She emphasized
church as a place you went to show off new
clothes and be seen on Sunday. (Keep in
mind the era. There was very little TV in small
towns at the time. Going to church on Sunday
was the highlight of your week—possibly
the biggest social event you had on your
calendar. It was more than obvious to me she
didn't care for the symbolism of it all.)

I believe we each have a higher power. You can call it a spirit, a Savior, universal energy, or some greater being. I call mine Jesus Christ. I was introduced to my faith early in life—not by my parents, but by our neighbors, Judy and Leonard. They were a great couple with four young children. Even though they had a full house, they made room to take my brother and me to church every Sunday and special occasions. They are also the basis of some of the fondest memories I have growing up. They truly were like family. In those years, we lived on a dead-end street in Mitchel, Illinois—just a few scattered houses with a cast full of characters: My best friend Carol and her numerous brothers and sisters; her amazing mom who held all of it together and still worked; her father who seemed so grumpy but would do anything for us kids. The list goes on. The best memories were created on that little dead-end street.

Grace Baptist Church in Granite City, Illinois, is where I first attended Sunday School, Vacation Bible School, learned about Jesus,

became saved and was baptized. I remember one Sunday in church, about age seven, the minister was calling members of the church who wanted to be saved to come to the altar. Once they got there, people were kneeling, and other people were praying with them.
I very vividly remember watching this take place and feeling moved to join them. I didn't understand it all, but before I realized what I was doing, there I was, walking to the front of the altar, kneeling down, and answering the question, "Do you accept Jesus Christ as your Savior?" I was nodding my head "Yes." Later, I remember thinking, "What was I thinking?" Truly, I was guided there by my Savior, and as I look back on my life, He has guided me many times along the way, preparing me and positioning me to receive the gifts He so graciously had planned for me.

Statistics suggest that more than half of the population is with a spouse or significant other for financial reasons, and I definitely fell into that percentage. After my first marriage, I married a man who had quickly come into my life. We didn't marry or even live together for several years, but I loved him and his big family.

After just a few months of marriage, we were expecting a baby boy, and he took a job that caused him to work nights seven days a week. We were a family that loved camping and outdoor activities. We didn't take a long vacation each year; we took several long weekends so we could enjoy several vacations. Those would soon end.

Just a few weeks into his new job, which he loved, I told him, "This job is going to be the death of our marriage." And that it was. We grew apart, fast. He became a recluse, eating dinner in the bedroom and going to bed soon after that, with no family interaction. With his best time to take off during the week, the kids and I could no longer join him on his fishing trips. That was OK with him because he had a few buddies he could go with.

Working such a crazy schedule, he had little time for family. Not only that, we became almost a burden to him. He was, for the most part, a loner, and he liked being his own boss in his new job. Life at home became harder. As the years went by, we became nothing more than roommates. The kids grew up and moved on, and the house became empty for the most part. We led two separate lives in the same home.

I poured myself into my work. I have always loved my job. My boss and I were creating several projects, and they were coming to fruition. We opened several dental assisting schools. As those bloomed, I was away more, setting up the schools and traveling a lot. With me gone more, my partner grew resentful of my time away. For me, work was a sanctuary from the negativity I was dealing with at home. And the more I worked, the harder life became at home. Planning my exodus became a mission that I worked on—diligently.

With my parents gone, my brother far
away, and my kids struggling to make lives
on their own, I was afraid. What if I failed?
Where would I go? Did I make enough
money to support myself and help out if my
children needed me? At that point, I just
wanted to survive.

I finally made the move and got out.

And then, I waited.

I waited to see what would happen.

Would I be OK on my own?

Would I fail?

Would I miss the home I'd had for over
twenty years?

Could I actually do this?

My fear brought me closer to my faith, as
I only had God to lean on and pour my

heart out to every day. I was (and still am) immensely grateful. I had a small two-bedroom apartment and walking in that door each day, I felt alive. I had sold everything I thought I needed. I wanted a fresh start, and *things* can always be replaced. My furnishings back then were sparse, but they were fresh and new, and I could breathe. I now had a sense of peace that I hadn't had in years.

Amazing things happen when you get rid of the negative relationships in your life. My fears made me even more determined to be successful in my new life. And my grateful heart and faith in the Lord led me to some pretty awesome opportunities. My life was blooming into something I could never have imagined. The weight of the stress and negativity was gone. It was replaced with new challenges, but *positive* challenges that made me stronger. And stronger is what I felt, *every single day*.

Part of my faith is believing that each of us is given a purpose greater than we can even imagine. I believe that God gave us so much potential, most of us haven't begun to tap into it. Your potential lives inside of you. You have to reach in and grab it; you have to take it. My God is a mighty God, and he created all of us with tremendous potential, but He wants us to go after it. He wants us to reach deep and find it in ourselves. If somebody gives you something, just hands you everything you have, then you begin to take things for granted; why do you have to work for it? It's always there. You appreciate things more if you work hard and earn them. Being handed everything sounds great, but if you don't ever have to work for anything, then you'll never know the satisfaction of earning it. You will never have pride in what you have accomplished.

Having faith and trusting in God is hard. It's *scary*. The unknowns. The what ifs. But what if you don't? What if you *don't* take a chance? What if I hadn't finally gone out on my own? Where would I be today?

When I was living in negativity, I wasn't leaning on God. I was consumed with hurt and anger. Oh, I've always kept my faith, but sometimes, when you are at your lowest, it's hard to see through the muck. I was blinded by it.

I think God took me out of it so I could see clearly again. I lean on Him every day now. Life is good, but I know where I have been. And even though I know where I'd like to go, I know that God has much bigger plans for me. He has much bigger plans for you, too. We hold ourselves back by not seeing the gifts we possess. We are the only limit to finding our own worth. We think small; God thinks *big*. Be a bigger thinker. Trust in Him to lead you to your gifts.

TIJA'S TIDBIT

"He who kneels before God can stand before anyone."

AUTHOR UNKNOWN

Put God first in your life, and He will bring you to amazing things.

CHAPTER 4

Laws That Protect You And Your Practice

Many people assume that the laws pertaining to doctors, hygienists, or assistants are universal, or the same in every state. Often, I see a post on social media asking about some law, and all kinds of opinions result. After about fifty replies, someone will finally ask, "What state are you in?" *BINGO!*

Never assume laws are universal. The laws are so different in every state it's unreal. Some states require dental assistants to have a radiology permit/license; some require an infection control permit/license. Some states want dental assistants to be certified, either within their state or through the Dental Assistant National Board (DANB). Some states offer expanded functions or expanded duties, and some do not. Some states require you to be a registered dental assistant (RDA) within that state. If you are an RDA in one state, you are *only* an RDA in that state. Some states recognize the RDA distinction, and others do not. Your RDA will not carry over to another state. If you can think of it, the law is probably different in just about every state.

I've heard someone say, "I took that in California. If you took it there, it is good anywhere." *Not true.* Don't ever think that just because you are experienced and have performed a function for years, your skill or credentials will carry over to another state. I don't care how experienced you are; if you move to a state where the practice is not allowed, then it's illegal, plain and simple. And practicing dentistry without a license is a felony which carries consequences—certainly fines, and potentially even jail time.

It's safe to assume that if you live and work in one state and move, then the duties you were allowed to perform in your previous state are no longer allowed in your new state. How do you find out? The great people at DANB have done all the work for you. Visit DANB. org, and right on the home page you will find a Search by State box. Select the state you're interested in, and you will find their requirements for dental assistants. DANB has this information for every state. Need more information? Don't rely on social media to get your information; talk to your state dental board. After all, while the legislature makes the laws, the dental boards are the ones who interpret and enforce state dental practice laws, so get the info straight from the horse's mouth. There is so much misinformation out there; if you take a question to social media, you will get 100 different opinions with no way to differentiate among them. Even your own team members will have their own ideas of what the laws are. Who's right?

Nitrous oxide certification is one function that is very different in each state. Some forbid allowing a dental assistant to monitor or be left alone with the patient while they are under nitrous oxide. Some states allow assistants to monitor with the doctor's supervision. Some states allow you to monitor with a certification of completion from a course approved by that state's dental board, and some states allow assistants to administer nitrous oxide either under the doctor's supervision or after a certificate of completion from an approved course. If you move from an administering state to a monitoring state, it is illegal for you to administer in your new state, no matter how much experience you have administering nitrous oxide. Don't try to keep up with all of the differences in regulations and laws; it's exhausting. Check DANB or your state dental practice act.

Likewise, in some states, you are covered under your doctor's professional liability insurance, and in others, only certain things are covered. I think it's always best to carry your own liability insurance. If you are a member of the American Dental Assistants

Association (ADAA) $50,000 worth of professional liability insurance is included at no cost with your membership, and it also covers liability regarding the Health Insurance Portability and Accountability Act (HIPAA).

Keep in mind that HIPAA and OSHA (Occupational Safety and Health Administration) compliance are beasts all their own when it comes to laws that govern us, and both require annual training on specific laws. I find that many offices lack education on these requirements or train only a designated person within the office. For HIPAA violations, keep in mind that the United States Department of Health and Human Services (HHS) will fine the offender, not necessarily just the doctor. If you have been properly trained and violate HIPAA policy, you can be fined. And speaking of HIPAA policy, does your office have one? Every office should, just like OSHA.

A hygienist once told me she didn't want to be trained because then she would be responsible for following the law; if she wasn't trained, and didn't know, she would be off the hook. *Yes, she actually said that*. I am not an attorney, but ignorance of the law is no excuse for not following it. You can, and may be, held responsible for what you are doing in an office and what you're not doing.

Because infection control is by far the most important thing we do in the office on a daily basis for our patients and ourselves, there is no room for error. If you don't know the law, educate yourself. The information is free and online for both HIPAA and OSHA. I always say it only takes one disgruntled patient or coworker to rock your world. There is only one way to do it: the right way.

"That's the way we've always done it" are the seven words I hate most. What do you do now that you have done the same way for ten, fifteen, twenty years? *Nothing*. Everything changes. When I was young, I would watch my mom eat cream cheese. In my mind, that was gross. But now? Now I *love* cream cheese. Even your taste buds change. You don't wear the same clothes or wear your hair the same way; why on earth would you do infection control the same way? In the thirty-seven years that I have been blessed to be in this profession, the changes I've seen have been extensive, especially in the area of infection control. It's been one of the fastest-evolving areas of our profession.

I was once in an office, and when I saw their procedure trays laid out, with instruments unpackaged and ready to go, I mentioned they really shouldn't do it that way. Their response? "Oh, Mary isn't going to like that."

You see, Mary was the lead assistant who had worked in the office for almost forty years. Mary had a routine, and she didn't want that routine interrupted. The other assistants didn't like the way things were done, but no one wanted to cross Mary.

Another time, assistants in an office were proud to show me how organized their instrument drawers were (and they truly *were*). When I asked why the instruments weren't wrapped, they said after sterilization, they *unwrapped them because they fit in the draws better*. I explained they couldn't do that—that the instruments had to stay in their packaging until the patient was seated. Like Mary, *they* didn't like their routine being messed with, either.

Often, you simply don't know what you don't know. Maybe other team members have no clue they are doing something in a way that's now outdated. Educate yourself and use what you have learned to make the changes necessary to be compliant. The CDC (Center for Disease Control) and OSAP (Organization for Safety, Asepsis and Prevention) are both amazing resources for infection control compliance. Acquire information from them and share your findings with your team members. Help them out by introducing them to new ideas. Just because someone doesn't agree with the guidelines is no reason not to follow them. You don't get to create your own rules.

We all have areas that need improvement, so find two or three things you can work on and concentrate on those. If you look at the bigger picture, you'll be overwhelmed. Work together as a team so that everyone is involved in making the changes; that way everyone feels like a part of the process. When the initial changes have been accomplished, find something else that needs improvement. Before long, you'll have a smoothly running office.

The bottom line is that laws are there to protect everyone: you, your patients, and the practice. I'd like to think that our doctors know the laws that pertain to us, but many times, they do not. Maybe they attended dental school in a different state. Maybe the laws have changed. Maybe they have the practice to run. Don't ever do something just because "My doctor said I could." If you don't know the laws or do not understand what is legal for you to do, it's up to you to educate yourself and not rely on anyone else. Don't allow something so important to just slip on by. You can be held accountable for your actions or lack thereof. Visit the DANB site and get the information. The organization continually keeps it updated *for you*.

TIJA'S TIDBIT

"Do what is right, not what is easy."

Author unknown

Integrity is everything.

CHAPTER 5

Who's In Charge Here?

OSHA, CDC, and HHS compliance are all federally mandated, with one notable difference among them. OSHA and HHS enforce *laws* that we are bound to follow, while the CDC issues *guidelines* for infection control. OSHA and HIPAA (administered by HHS) require us to be annually updated on rules and regulations; the CDC does not require anything of us. Now, that's where many offices leave it, but that's not the entire story. You see, many of our states' dental practice acts pick up the CDC guidelines and codify them into law. If you violate a CDC guideline, you may very well be violating a law within your own state's dental practice act. And in some states, yearly review and continuing education for infection control are mandatory. Don't brush off the CDC guidelines as nonregulatory; your state's dental board takes them very seriously.

The CDC is a great resource for all things infection control. Another great resource is the Organization for Safety, Asepsis, and Prevention, or OSAP. I had the privilege of attending one of the organization's Infection Control Boot Camps, a seminar held annually. It is an amazing three-day course. As much as I know about infection control, my mind was blown before lunch on the first day. It is a great learning experience, very well put together, with amazing speakers and classes. If you are serious about infection control, OSAP Boot Camp is for you. The group also holds an annual conference; become a member and enjoy all the benefits of learning.

I previously mentioned there is only one way to do infection control: the right way. Taking care of the public's health is very serious; it's the most important thing we do on a daily basis. Consider this: who are your patients? In *my* practice, it's my family, my friends, and the patients who have become friends after years of placing confidence in my team. I don't want to take any chances with my grandkids' health, or with *anyone's* health, so I want to make sure that everything is done the right way, so I don't jeopardize their health and safety. It's not just our patients whose health and safety is at risk; it's ours and our team's. Having strict infection control protocols in place and following them can prevent illness, injury, the spread of disease, and even death.

In my many visits to dental offices I've heard about and witnessed several lapses in infection control protocols. On more than one occasion, I've been told that there isn't enough time to do everything the guidelines propose properly. Now, let's look at that statement more deeply. Are you saying there is not enough time to do everything properly to prevent illness and injury, so you are going to just hurry along and improvise, so you can get to the next patient? Who *says* you're in a hurry? The front desk? The doctor?

Your teammates? Each patient deserves and expects a practice to be 100 percent compliant in infection control. Don't believe me? Ask your patients what they think.

How about you? Do you want to go to a healthcare facility that doesn't follow strict standards? How about going into a restaurant that's not approved by the board of health? Sound appetizing? Not really. So why would we think that patients should be treated in a substandard way? If I'm a patient in my practice (and I am), I want to know that my teammates are following protocol to the letter to keep all of us safe.

One of the biggest failures I notice in the field is a lack of personal protective equipment (PPE). *We hate it.* "The mask fogs up our glasses; we get hot while the front desk is freezing; when we leave the operatory, it's easier to just move our mask down to our chin; and you want me to wear *all of that* in sterilization? I just took it all off!"

Yes, it's true, you must be *fully PPEd up* when processing instruments in the sterilization area, but it's *for your own good.* Those laws and regulations are there for one reason, and it's not just to annoy you. The guidelines are there to keep you safe. Think about what you take home to your family.

I was recently speaking to a packed room about dental assisting laws, and I was fortunate enough to have a doctor in attendance who was not only a dentist but also an attorney. During the break, I had several people come up and ask questions. Several wanted to talk about IV sedation and the regulations governing it. Since I wasn't in my state and I was not familiar with local governing law, I waited until everyone was seated and asked for the help of the dentist/lawyer. When I asked him about laws governing IV sedation in that state, his response was, "There is no question. It is illegal for a dental assistant to perform IV sedation in this state." With that, you could have heard a pin drop. At least fifteen people had shared with me during the break that they were sedating patients, yet none of them knew it was illegal. They were all "doing what their doctors told them to do."

Another phrase I hate hearing is "I've been practicing (amount of years) and nothing has ever happened." And I can say, in my thirty-seven plus years, I've not had many emergencies. I have also had only *one* car accident, and yet I still carry car insurance. I've never used my homeowner's insurance, but I'm not about to drop that. You see, accidents happen *all the time*. They come without warning, sometimes in big ways and sometimes in small ways. Being prepared and using proper infection control protocols is key to successfully keeping our patients and our team safe when accidents *do* happen.

Your state's dental practice act covers the functions and procedures that dental assistants are allowed to perform. As previously noted, the differences among the states are huge, so never assume something is allowed; it may not be.

If you feel uneasy about something you've been asked to do, never feel you have to do it just because you were told to. Check with your state. Ask the people who make the laws. And don't do something just because it's always been done that way. Many times, it's just ignorance of the law. Finding the right answers and sharing with everyone on the team is the best way to help everyone.

Record-keeping for patients is something we sometimes don't do as well as we should. Clinical chart notes are not just used by your practice as a diary of sorts for what has happened in the past; these may possibly be used by another dentist and can serve as evidence by the dental board or in a court of law. Dentists and dental hygienists are taught how to write chart notes, but many times, it's the dental assistant in the practice who actually makes the chart notes, and we aren't always taught the dynamics of writing accurate and well-defined clinical chart notes. The rule is to be as detailed as possible. You simply can't make enough notes when it comes to documenting the patient's dental visit. It's also very important to not use abbreviations or slang when constructing your clinical notes. Sure, your team knows what you are talking about; you have your own in-office language, and you can decipher what the notes are. But what if those notes are called into question or are sent to another doctor out-of-state when your patient moves away? Could someone else, not familiar with your "practice language," be able to comprehend what you wrote? Have your doctor construct a clinical notes template that you can use as a guide for constructing complete and accurate clinical chart notes.

According to the U.S. Department of Labor website, there are approximately 320,000 dental assistants in the United States. Arguably over half of our workforce has never been formally trained. They are on-the-job-trained, and seriously, there is nothing wrong with that. Whether you were trained in a yearlong program, a shorter proprietary program, or trained on the job, we are all dental assistants. It's what you do and how much you have invested in yourself since you began working in a dental office that sets you apart. So, there is simply no reason to not be educated.

Ethics is something that morally defines us. It's a set of choices we make every single day, not just in our career life, but in everything we do. We are faced with one dilemma after another, day in and day out. Not cutting corners on infection control, showing up for work on time, not being the first one out the door, jumping in to help a teammate whose lunch hour is approaching and is in danger of running over. Ethical choices make us the better person, help us do the right thing, and give our patients the best possible care we can give.

TIJA'S TIDBIT

"I follow three rules: do the right thing, do the best you can, and always show people you care."

LOU HOLTZ

Be true to yourself first.

CHAPTER 6

So You Think You're A Professional?

I hear the cry over and over: Dental assistants want respect and to be treated like the dental professionals we are. And it is so true. Now, all we have to do is act like it.

I've made my share of mistakes in my career, so let's explore some of the many mistakes we dental assistants can make that are doing more harm to our profession than good.

I once had a teammate who looked as if she grabbed her scrubs out of the laundry basket and threw them on. The scrubs were so wrinkled, wrinkles were the only things you saw when you looked at her. I'm awful at taking my clothes out of the dryer and hanging them up right away, so I completely understand the wrinkles. I *don't* understand going ahead and putting them on and wearing them like that. Get out that iron, or start that dryer again and get those wrinkles out. Maybe try throwing a wet cloth in the dryer; it will create some steam in there to do the job. (Got a steam dryer? Then there is no excuse.)

I also don't understand scrubs that get *walked on.* I'm 5'8, so I've never had this problem, but if your scrubs are that long, *hem them.* Let's say it's raining out, you're rushing into the office, and it's pouring. Because your scrubs are too long, they have dragged on the ground in the mud and are now nasty. You bring back your first patient, and as you walk in front to show the patient to the operatory, the patient looks down and sees your nasty, dirty scrub pants. How much confidence does that patient now have in your practice being *clean*? How much confidence does that patient have in *you*? If you want to be considered a professional, you have to look the part and act the part.

I was helping a doctor perform job interviews for a hygiene position a few years ago. It had been raining all day and had begun to thunder and lightning. As the doctor and I stood at the windows of the strip-mall location, watching the downpour, a woman came running up to the building. At one point, one of the flip-flops she was wearing flew off across the parking lot as she kept running. Thinking she was going into one of the nearby stores, we giggled at the sight. Suddenly, she opened the door and exclaimed, "I'm here for my interview."

Flip-flops? Seriously?

Needless to say, she did not get hired.

An interview, be it on the phone or in person, is the first impression a practice gets of you. So be professional, dress the part, and be prepared. You want to put your best foot forward (no pun intended).

The interview—that's a big subject in itself. When you get a chance to interview, being prepared is huge when it comes to looking professional. Gather a list of questions you'd like to have answered. Remember, they aren't just interviewing you; you are also interviewing them. Are these people you would even want to work for? Do your research. Look into the office you're about to go into. Check them out. Visit their website. Find out their hours. Are they hours you want? Where are they located? Would you have to travel to get to one office, or do they have multiple locations? Don't ever assume that a potential employer offers holiday pay, sick, or vacation pay. Those are things you want to ask. Is health insurance important to you? Does the employer offer it? What about continuing education? Does the office pay for it? Pay a portion of it? Encourage it? Does your state offer expanded functions? Is that something this office promotes? Are you interested in that? Going on an interview isn't just about looking your best to get the job; make sure the job is *right for you.*

When I had just graduated high school,
I began taking classes at the community
college. With spare time on my hands, I
enthusiastically joined Mary Kay cosmetics as
a salesperson. Right away, I dove into training.
These women had years of experience, and I
was eager to learn from them. One of the very
first training seminars covered how we should
dress when making phone calls. Our trainer
told us to get up, take a shower, fix our hair
and makeup, get on our best dress, and then
get on that phone and make calls.

What? You mean I was going to sit on the
phone all day long and make calls, and *I had
to get dressed up for that*? I thought she
was out of her mind. "I'm going to wear my
sweatpants," I thought. What I didn't quite
understand then was that how you feel on the
outside elevates your *insides*, and vice-versa.

When do you feel your best? How about
when you're getting ready to go out with

friends? You get dressed up, fix your hair and your makeup. You feel *great*! That's what the trainer was talking about that day, and that's how you should go to work every day—feeling fantastic. When you look good, you feel good, and that puts a smile on your face. You radiate from the inside, and it sets your mood for the day. And when you radiate and feel great, those around you will catch the good vibes, too. It's contagious.

Ever go to work, and the Debbie Downer of the bunch is in a bad mood? That bad mood will spread like wildfire, and soon the entire office is having a bad day. But imagine what it would be like if you went to work happy, feeling fantastic? That will *also* spread to others in the office, and everyone will have a better day. You can either elevate those around you or bring them down. Focus on having a positive attitude and lifting others up, and you can do amazing things. The old saying, "Attitude is everything" is cheesy but true. Thinking positively will bring about positive changes. Focus on the negative, and you have worse days.

Ever notice on social media that the same people are the ones that always have things go wrong? They are always complaining about this or that, how they only have bad luck. That's because they only focus on the bad. If you take a look at my social media, you will seldom see me post negative things. It's not that I'm perfect and bad things don't happen to me; it's that I *choose* not to make them public, or to air my dirty laundry for everyone to see. Likewise, when you go into your practice and complain about your home life, or post negative things on social media, you make yourself a target for gossip. Don't give anyone that power over you. Keep your drama to yourself and focus on what you're there for. Focus on your career and how you can make your day better. You'll be amazed at how much better you feel.

How much continuing education is required of you annually? Depending on your state and your certifications, it can vary. A true professional never stops learning. This career of mine has changed immensely through the years, and I've seen huge changes in all facets of dentistry. Keeping up with all of it requires dedication to continually learning. If your practice doesn't promote continual learning, I highly suggest you demand it of yourself. If you want to further your career, reach a little higher, and accomplish more. Never stop learning.

TIJA'S TIDBIT

"Without hard work and discipline, it is difficult to be a top professional."

JAHANGIR KHAN

Nothing worth having is ever easy, but the satisfaction you'll get when you reach your accomplishments will propel you to greater things.

CHAPTER 7

Each One Of You Is A Leader

Dental assistants seldom see themselves as leaders, but why not? It's true that many of us don't hold a license or permit, but those pieces of paper don't make anyone a leader. A great leader is one who inspires others, lifts them up, takes responsibility for his or her actions, is honest and passionate. All in all, a genuinely good person who cares for others. Dental assistants have those traits.

It's said that great leaders adapt to change. Wow—I don't know any professional who can adapt to change like we can. We can multitask with the best of them, and we are the superheroes of the dental office. Can doctors work without hygienists? Absolutely, they can. Is it smart? No, not really. Can they work without dental assistants? *No.* And for proof, walk into the office on any given Monday, where the doctor has just seen an emergency in the office over the weekend and has left a huge mess. *You know what I'm talking about.* Drawers open, a mess in the operatory, no clue where anything is. So, why don't we feel like leaders? Because if you are like me, you've had this little voice inside your head telling you that you are not good enough. The truth is, we all are leaders and have something to contribute; we just need to believe in ourselves.

Most of the time, we feel as if we are in the lowest position on the totem pole, and that we are not respected. But I also believe that's a burden we place on ourselves. We overthink and underappreciate our own selves, and that, of course, is reflected to others.

Ever go to a seminar and hear some amazing new ideas? You are *stoked*. It's like the speaker had been looking inside your windows and was giving that seminar just to you. You go back to the office on Monday, and you are ready to take on the world. The team meeting is tomorrow, you have organized all your ideas, and you are ready to present them. Negative Nelly shoots down every idea you have, but some of the team still seem to be on board. You come up with great action plans on how to implement the suggestions, and off you go. Four weeks later, you gather at the next team meeting, and not one person can remember what you were going to do, who was going to do it, or even why you all got so excited in the first place. You were all gung-ho, but the fizz has faded.

When you have those amazing ideas and bring them to the team, create an action plan and pass out the duties it will take to *make it happen*. You want to hit that finish line together, with everyone's action and input. When everyone has a piece of the pie and is involved in the project, it will flow much smoother. But it doesn't end there. The hardest part is the follow-through and making sure everyone has done their part. If we get all excited about a new protocol, piece of equipment, or way to make life easier, but *nobody takes responsibility* to make it happen, get educated, or implement the protocols, then instead of growing, we have taken a step backward. Having great ideas but never seeing them through is frustrating, and it takes a leader to see ideas through to fruition.

It's important to revisit the action plan at each monthly meeting, or even in the morning at team huddles. Keep in mind the enthusiasm you first had for new ideas and instill it whenever you can in everyone else. Take the lead.

I always was the early one, arriving anywhere from thirty minutes to an hour before scheduled open. I even had a boss once tell me, "You know I don't pay you until quarter till the hour, don't you?" I had to laugh because I *did* know that. Coming in early, however, even when I wasn't getting paid, gave me time to get my day in order, organize my schedule, and be on top of anything that might happen. It just made me feel better. If that made my day flow better, then I was willing to do it. To this day, I'm an early bird anywhere I go. If I'm on time, to me that's late. But if I'm a half-hour early, I can find calm in my day. We are all different, but establishing a routine and getting organized are great ways to stand out as a leader.

I visit several pages on social media, and most of them are for dental assistants. So many times, I see derogatory comments on different posts. Strong women and men encourage others; they do not tear them down. What would happen if we spoke to our coworkers the way many of us speak on social media? I believe they would call it bullying.

Keep in mind that everyone may not know everything you know. Maybe you've been in this profession for years, and you have a new assistant in your practice asking questions. It's frustrating. You end up doing things because it's easier for you to do them than to explain what you are doing and why you are doing them. Trust me when I say I've been there. But please remember you were once that young assistant who craved knowledge. New assistants want to learn, too, and if we keep putting them down, they will never grow. Being a leader means you help others grow to become leaders, too. Take time to teach them, share your passion, and give, give, give. True integrity gives you a reputation that others can trust and depend on. The more you help others see their potential, the more you will grow as a person.

Being a leader also means doing the right thing, even when nobody is around to see it. Cutting corners isn't in the plan when it comes to patient care and ensuring the safety and well-being of our teammates. If you are only doing something to make yourself look good, you're doing it for the wrong reason. And always focusing on how great *you* are, instead of how great your *team* is, diminishes people's respect for you. (Remember, there is no I in team.)

True leaders don't whine when they don't get their way. They don't indulge in negative behavior and pout to get attention. Real leaders don't seek attention—but attention will find you because people will be attracted to you.

Most importantly, true leaders care for others, and dental assistants excel when it comes to caring for others. None of us got into this profession because of the fortune or fame. We came into this profession for our own reasons, and we stay because we truly love and care for people. We love helping others and genially give from our hearts. We are our doctors' right hands, and we go out of our way to help them any way we can. We sit alongside them, and we can read them like books. We know what they need when they need it. When it comes to sitting chairside, we know them better than they do.

You are a leader.

You are a rock star dental assistant, and *you* are *amazing*.

Reach deep inside of you and look for the leader I know is there. You can do amazing things if you just set your mind to it.

TIJA'S TIDBIT

"Great leaders don't set out to be a leader; they set out to make a difference. It's never about the role—always about the goal."

LISA HAISHA

When you do what is right, you will attract great things.

CHAPTER 8

Pet Peeves And Communication

We all have our own pet peeves: things patients or teammates say can drive us up the wall. For me, one is going to the reception area where a patient has been waiting to call them back, only for them to ask, "Can I use the restroom first?" Better yet is when I go out to call them back, and they are on their cell phone and hold up a finger as if to say, "Just a minute." Seriously? Maybe you have a team member who is *always* late or one who always has to leave early; maybe it's the same person. What if the doctor is the one who is always running late? What do you do when it's the boss?

Whatever our pet peeves are, they get under our skin and crawl.

How do you handle them? What makes you reach your boiling point? At what point do you get fed up? How you handle pet peeves speaks volumes about you and can dictate how your day flows. For whatever reason, negative energy spreads faster than positive energy, so if you're having a bad day, you've potentially now infected your teammates with a *crappy* attitude. It's time to take a deep breath and clear that negative energy off of you. Identify your personal pet peeves and remember you can't change other people; you can only change yourself. Uncover those triggers and find ways to deal with them. Step out the back door or escape to the restroom. (Our boss provides copious amounts of chocolate in case of such emergencies.) Take a few minutes for yourself, so you don't explode. It's not healthy for you or your teammates.

It is said, "The biggest communication problem is we don't listen to understand; we listen to reply."

We know what that person needs, and we can't wait for them to stop talking so we can tell them. We are experts at pointing out each other's flaws.

We love to seek weaknesses in others. We all have that flaw, and some people love nothing more than to find it and capitalize on it. If we spent that much energy focusing on other's people strengths, supporting them, and encouraging them, just *think* what would happen. Think of what great things could happen if you did something nice for your teammates each day, and then for your patients. That attitude would be infectious and soon spread to others. Your practice would flourish, and you'd have the best working environment ever.

I know it's easy to say "Think positive," but it's so useful. At my lowest points with my personal life, I felt like my work was my sanctuary. Part of who I am today is because I dove into my work to escape my personal life. It's how I handled my life and circumstances. Having a positive attitude isn't just a cheesy saying; it truly will lift your day and make it better.

What about the teammate who is *always* on a cell phone? Back in the day, we had these amazing little rooms called darkrooms (back before photography went digital). The darkroom was our little office sanctuary. We kept our snacks in there, and it was awesome, because if anyone wanted us, we simply said, "Don't open that door," even when it was really OK to do so. With the advent of technology, however, the darkroom is, for the most part, a thing of the past (sigh). So now, if we want some private time in the middle of a hectic day, we go into the restroom, and of course, we take our phones. We catch up on emails and text messages, take selfies— whatever we do in there—and catch a few moments of quiet time.

(Did you know when you flush a toilet, it's said that it sprays up to six feet? And did you realize that most public restrooms don't have a lid on the toilet? When you are done with your business, where do you put your phone while you're washing your hands? The back of the toilet, maybe? And then you flush. Here is an interesting study from the U.K. published in October 2011. Researchers from the London School of Hygiene & Tropical Medicine and from Queen Mary, University of London analyzed 780 swab samples—390 from mobile phones and 390 from the hands that used them—in twelve cities across the United Kingdom. Sixteen percent of both hands and phones were contaminated with E. coli, potentially illness-causing bacteria found in fecal matter (also said to be the leading cause of adult acne). So basically, one in six of us has poop on our phones. There are over one million germs living on those phones: eighteen times more bacteria than a toilet seat. We won't put our faces on the toilet seat, yet we don't mind rubbing that nasty cell phone all over it. And do you give your phone to your kids or grandkids? Yup, now you get it.)

I digress.

Part of what makes a great dental assistant is listening. Listen to the patient's needs and wants. Sometimes you have to read between the lines. Both verbal and nonverbal communication are huge when communicating with patients. A patient may tell you he or she is OK, but if you look at the hands, they are locked tight, fists clenched, almost what we call "white-knuckle syndrome:" their fingers are locked so tight, their knuckles turn white. What they say verbally and what they say with their bodies are sometimes two different things. Take time to *really* listen to your patient. Your patients don't know what we know. They don't know what services and treatments are available to them. Listen to what they say, but don't hesitate to talk about services they may be interested in. We spend more time with the patients than any other team member, so use that time to educate them and open up avenues that can make them feel better about themselves.

Patients can smell a bad attitude and tension in the office. They can tell when something in our practice isn't right. If you are in an altercation with a teammate, trust me, the entire office will know it. You won't have to tell the patients; they will see the handwriting on the wall.

Patients hate coming to the dental office, and that's an understatement. Over the years I've heard patients say such things as, "I'd rather have a baby than come here." (I've had two babies, and going to the dentist was a piece of cake compared to childbirth.) It's safe to say, for the most part, our patients are afraid, uncomfortable, and would rather be someplace else. So, if there is tension in the air, you're not doing much to ease fears—you're doing just the opposite. We spend more time with our work families than we do with our own families, so working as a team and getting along is imperative to create a great atmosphere, one that patients want to be a part of.

The key to working as a team is to keep lines of communication open, listen to what others have to say, and consider their input. Remember, the world doesn't revolve around you, so keep your mind open and allow other ideas to be put to the test. Who knows; you may love what somebody else came up with. If you aren't getting along with a teammate, find time at the end of the day to talk like adults and air your grievances. Never attempt this in front of patients; set aside your differences until you have time to talk with each other and not *at* each other. Don't allow yourself to reach your boiling point, and if you do, go to the darkroom (um, bathroom) and take a few minutes to calm yourself.

We all love to complain—we need this, we need that, this is wrong, that's wrong. We can always point out what could be done better, but how would you change things if it were up to you? I don't mind if my teammates come to me with a problem, but I also want them to bring a solution. Will their suggested solution be the answer to our problem? Not always. But only complaining leaves the problem in that realm: complaints. If you truly want to change things and make things better, come up with ways to solve them. Never bring me a problem without a solution.

We are a team, and as such, I want all of us working together to create the practice of our dreams. It's not about me, or our boss, or the front desk or hygiene team. It's all about those patients and creating the best possible patient experience we can.

At the end of the day, don't allow your pet peeves or lack of communication to ruin your day. Our work family is just that—family. We will argue and fight and make up because that's what families do. None of us are perfect, so learn to laugh at the mistakes. Work on that attitude and begin each day with giving. You'll love the way you feel.

TIJA'S TIDBIT

"Smile—it's the best thing you can do to irritate those who wish to destroy you."

AUTHOR UNKNOWN

Always be the bigger person; don't allow anyone to bring you down to their level.

CHAPTER 9

Choose Your Words Wisely

"Let's give it a shot," I said, and I can still see my boss's face reacting in horror to my inelegant words. I wasn't talking about a *shot*. I was talking about going ahead with the *procedure* we were doing. That was way back when, and I quickly learned never to let those words fly out of my mouth again. There are just some things we shouldn't say in our line of work, and yet sometimes, we just can't stop it.

I had a young intern in my office once and was telling her how patients hate coming in, so I like to talk about their favorite subject—themselves. It's a topic they know a lot about, and if you can get them talking about their families, their vacations, or their pets, they seem to relax more. On Monday or Tuesday, you will always hear me asking a patient, "How was your weekend?" On Wednesday or Thursday, you'll hear me ask, "Got big plans for the weekend?" They get to talking and suddenly, they relax. They feel comfortable. The young intern listened intently to what I was saying—or so I thought. She brought a patient back, asked about her weekend, and after the patient told her all of her wonderful plans, the patient then asked, "What about yours?"

That was the moment I wished I could go back in time and interrupt the space-time continuum to alter her words to change the outcome.

"My baby daddy's girlfriend went into labor last night at 3:00 a.m. and I had to get the kid from the hospital, and the girlfriend hates me, so she was yelling at me to get the hell out of there, so I had to take the kid and leave. I haven't slept all night."

Looking back on that scene, it's as if it's replaying in slow motion and I'm trying to stop her from talking. The look on the patient's face was pure confusion.

I gathered myself, managed to close my mouth, and asked the intern to come with me. I explained to her that the patient *really didn't want or expect* to hear about her drama, and now that she had told the patient she hadn't slept all night, the patient didn't have much confidence in her. I would be doing the procedure, and she could shadow. I *believe* she saw how using those words was wrong; sometimes we just don't think about our words. They just come flying out of our mouths.

Choose your words carefully. Remember, we are professionals, and our patients see us as such. Keep as much of your personal life (or at least drama) out of the operatory.

It's critically important for our patients to have confidence in us and the relationships we build. They must believe in us and trust us to care for them and their families. Building that confidence happens over time, and it's all about using the proper words, taking time to talk to them, and listening to them. I have the *worst memory on earth*. When patients come in, however, I ask about the puppy the patient just got when they were in last, or the vacation they were getting ready to take the last time they were with us. They all think I have the most amazing memory and I am so sweet to remember them, out of all of our patients; the truth is, I wish I *could* remember, but the real reason I can recall all of that is because I take *amazing* notes.

Patients don't know if we do amazing dentistry. Have you ever had a patient applaud the dentist because a MOD looked absolutely amazing? Or compliment the team on how well a sealant was placed? No. Our patients only know how they were treated when they walked in the door. They know how you made them feel inside. There is a dentist on every corner. We all do dentistry—fillings, crowns, cleanings. What sets us apart is our customer service. Patients remember Mary up front always has a smile on her face, or the hygienist who is so sweet and always does an amazing job. They remember the assistant who takes so much time with them and remembers them. They only know how your team makes them feel when they are there. If everyone on our team does something to make each patient have a great experience, our practices flourish. Patients send their friends and family to us. That's *internal marketing,* and you can't buy that kind of advertising. Customer service is an area all of us need to be our best at and make each patient feel welcome.

Being professional means choosing our words carefully. There are just some things we should never discuss in the practice. We have patients from all walks of life: Different religions, different politics, you name it. So being respectful of each other is one of the most important things we can do.

There are some subjects we just shouldn't discuss in the dental office. We should always keep it light and never get too deep into controversial conversations. We all have different views on subjects about which we have deeply held value conflicts, but it's best to just focus on our patients, their needs, and how we can create a great patient experience.

I once had an assistant pull me into a room. She was waiting for the doctor to come in and she had a little five-year-old boy in the chair. When I entered the room, she said to me, "Can you believe his Mom and Dad told him there is no Santa Claus?" I'm sure she was expecting me to jump in and agree with her that there is, in fact, a Santa Claus.

Whether you believe in Santa Claus or not is not up to her or me. This child's parents had clearly not celebrated Santa Claus in their family traditions. It wasn't this assistant's place to tell this child his parents were wrong.

I just left the room and later told her maybe his parents didn't recognize Santa, and we shouldn't tell kids their parents are wrong. I hope she got it. We all have different beliefs, and not one of us is wrong.

I once was told, years ago, that there was a hygienist in a practice who, when the doctor treatment-planned the patient, waited for the doctor to leave the room and would then tell the patient if the hygienist felt the treatment was really needed or not. Unfortunately, I've not heard this once, but a handful of times. I even once overheard an assistant in my own practice telling a patient a crown the doctor had suggested wasn't really needed. My advice to anyone in a practice who does not agree with the doctor, or feels the doctor isn't doing a great job planning treatment, is to go find employment elsewhere. You have to support your doctor. Your team must be on the same page and work together for the patient's oral and overall health. If you are disagreeing with the doctor, then find another job, not only for yourself but for the practice. Don't ever work for someone you don't believe in. That's a stressful situation— one I have only found myself in once, and I didn't work there long. In good conscience, I couldn't continue to work there. I wasn't doing any favors to the doctor, the practice, the patients, or myself. Remember, you're not tied to any particular practice. Our profession is one of the fastest-growing professions there is. We are in demand. Don't ever feel as if you have to stay in a position for any reason. There are other jobs out there. You will find another one.

Keep in mind HIPAA rules and regulations. It's just not a HIPAA violation to discuss some things; it's also an ethical situation. It's not up to you to discuss patient care with anyone else. It's the patient's private information. We need to respect that. Keep patient information on a need-to-know basis and never discuss any patient's treatment in front of others. It's not just illegal, it's unethical too.

TIJA'S TIDBIT

"Three things you can't recover in life: the word after it's said, the moment after it's missed, and the time after it's gone"

AUTHOR UNKNOWN

Words can either do damage or heal. Choose your words wisely.

CHAPTER 10

Creating Value In Yourself

How exactly do you create value? How can you make yourself more valuable to your practice—and more importantly, more valuable to yourself?

I love to tell the story of how much my doctor hates making dentures. I mean, he *hates* it! He blamed the lab technician for not making dentures right; of course, the lab technician blamed him. He seemed to get angrier with each denture try-in. There was always something wrong, including getting cases back on time. It was so frustrating for me to watch a denture appointment. My doctor would shake his head behind his mask, and I knew he wasn't happy.

As dental assistants, it's our job to fix. We want to fix what is wrong in the office, especially when it comes to our doctors. We want to fix it and make it right. It's what we do. So, I wanted to fix this denture problem. I just wasn't sure exactly how to do it.

In the state of Missouri, where I practice, we have an expanded-functions permit for removable prosthodontics, and several years prior to this, I had obtained that permit. However, my doctor never allowed me to perform the duties because he always wanted to, so I had never fully utilized my training.

When I saw the frustration mounting and then him saying, "I'm never making another denture again," I knew I had to jump into action. It had been so long since training, though, I really had forgotten what to do. I needed to be retrained. I had to get educated.

I began by contacting a good friend, Dan, who was a removable lab technician in Colorado. I remember asking him, "Where do I start?" I felt I had forgotten everything and no idea where to begin. He suggested a series of videos he had and sent them to me right away. He also suggested I get in touch with a friend of his, a lab tech he knew to be an outstanding instructor. I watched the videos, and with Dan's permission, headed to Colorado to shadow him in his office to learn all I could. I contacted the other lab technician and began using him for my work, asking him every question I could. Both of these gentlemen were a huge help to me in helping me learn and grow.

In the state of Missouri with my permit in removable prosthetics, I could now handle many of the duties we needed to make a denture or partial. The next patient who needed a denture came in, and I was ready. Together with my doctor, we made a beautiful denture. We each taught the other something making that first denture together, and we have never stopped asking questions.

Now, our dentures are beautiful. We take time in making them, creating each one to fit the personality of the patient, something we didn't take time to do previously; we simply didn't know enough about the process. Not only that, but we realized that our lab technician was a part of our team, there to help us succeed together. By becoming educated, I was able to fix the problem and frustrations with making dentures.

As it turned out, I can honestly say the problems we were having weren't just with the lab we were using at the time. We were a big part of the problem. We simply weren't giving them enough information for them to make a quality denture. And the lab wasn't asking us the questions it needed to in order to correct the situation. Lack of communication? Very much so. Communication between lab and office is essential. Lab personnel are a part of your team. They are so knowledgeable and can help you so much more than what we often give them credit for. Learn from them.

I became an important part of the denture-making process, created value in my practice and with my doctor. Do you really think my boss wants to go back to doing it alone? *Never!* He loves that I jumped in and took over in an area he hated. He appreciates the fact that I was proactive and took the time to educate myself. I created value in me.

Creating value in yourself is about finding what is weak, finding what needs to be fixed, and doing it. Every office has a weak link, whether it is communication, sterilization, organization, or other areas within a dental assistant's scope of practice. What makes *your* day frustrating? What is the one thing at work you "hate"? Identify it and find a way to fix it.

Now it's easy to point out what needs to be done. At many team meetings, everyone sits around and talks and nothing is ever accomplished. We're all gung-ho and going to change the world. One week later, we can't even remember what it was we wanted to do. Therefore, follow-through becomes

more important than the actual project itself.
Create an action plan. Create a problem log.
Create a record of exactly what the issue is
and how you intend to fix it. Then work on it.
If you keep putting issues aside, then you'll
never get it done. Remember, not only are
you fixing a problem, you are creating value
in yourself, and you simply must make time
for that.

One of the greatest ways to create value in
yourself is to find ways to save the office
money. Now, this is not an invitation to find
a way to "cut corners." Infection control, for
example, is the most important thing we do
every day, and there is *no way* to cut corners
on protecting our patients and ourselves.
There are, however, many things you can do
to lower your overhead.

In dentistry, the cost of overhead is higher
than any other profession. The average office
runs beyond its means. A good rule of thumb
is 5 to 7 percent of the office's overhead

expense should be supplies. If you aren't there, there are many ways to get you there.

I'm a firm believer in another kind of teammate: your sales rep. We don't typically look at our sales reps as such, but trust me, they are there to help you succeed. When your practice succeeds, so do the sales reps, so allow them in and let them help you! Have conversations with them; are there products you can use as alternatives to other, costlier products that do the same thing? Is there a new and improved product on the market? Can you have samples? Is there an opportunity to have a lunch-and-learn to see new materials? If your sales reps can't answer your questions, they will get ahold of people who can. Now, every product that gets introduced to you won't necessarily work in your practice, but you won't know that until you try it, and in the process, you may find some amazing new or unique products.

Another big mistake many practices make is over-ordering. Sure, your supply room looks great if it's full of shiny new products, all neat and organized. But when I see that in an office, all I see is money sitting there on the shelf. While you don't want to run out of supplies, you certainly don't need a room stocked full of them. When you order supplies, you also get invoices, which are due at the end of each month. If those invoices aren't paid in full, then a usual 1.5 percent (or higher) finance fee is placed on the statement. So, no matter how much you think you "save," are you really saving *anything* if the statement can't be paid in full and has a finance fee placed on it?

Many supply companies today can have product orders delivered in twenty-four to forty-eight hours once you place the order. Set a budget and do your best to stick with it. You'll need your doctor to help you to establish this number; it's a percentage based on production. The budget can keep you in line. If you find yourself going over each month, review your expectations of the budget, or the reality of what supplies you are actually using. If you find that you are always under, then *lower the budget.*

I personally order once a week. It allows me to keep an eye out for the budget, see what products I use up the quickest and gives me better control of that storeroom. Since I order once a week, I can see what we use the most or least. And since I can get my products in just a day or two, we never run out. Setting a budget and sticking to it will help you manage your supply area efficiently.

Don't be wasteful, either. Keeping a close eye on the usage of bond, among other things, will cut cost tremendously. Think of it as your own money, because when the doctor saves, it leaves room for other to things, such as much-needed equipment, or even team bonuses.

TIJA'S TIDBITS

"You don't get paid for the hour. You get paid for the value you bring to the hour."

JIM ROHN

Don't expect a raise because you feel as if you deserve it. Perspective is everything.

CHAPTER 11

The Buck Stops Here

The phrase "Pass the buck" refers to passing blame on to someone else. We love to point fingers and not accept blame ourselves. We hate being wrong. We will gladly pass the buck. The only problem is, many times we try to pass it when in fact we *are* to blame and just don't want to accept responsibility for it. We hate being in trouble and will avoid that all we can; it's human nature.

"The buck stops here" was a phrase Harry S. Truman, the thirty-third president of the United States, believed in. He even placed a sign with this slogan on his desk in the White House. His logic was that he had, as President, difficult decisions to make, and that he would accept full responsibility for them. He wasn't going to "pass the buck" to anyone. If he was wrong, he would accept responsibility.

When something wrong happens in my practice, as office manager, it *must* be my fault. Maybe I didn't train someone to do the assigned job. Maybe I expected too much, and the person didn't feel as if he or she could talk to me about it. How did I fail this person? I can always point that finger back at me; the buck stops here.

When you attempt to pass the buck and avoid responsibility, it says something about you, and usually not a *good* something. And if you're passing it and you know you had a part in the matter, most of the time, someone else already knows, and that doesn't make you look good. As a matter of fact, if you make a mistake and will admit it, most people will have more respect for you than if you try to pass the buck. We all make mistakes. That's a given.

They say that hindsight is 20/20, and if you take a look back on your life right now, I'm sure there are things you wish you had or hadn't done. I know there are things I regret, things I wish I hadn't done. If I had to do my life over again, I would certainly work harder to reach my goals sooner. I believe that mistakes are nothing more than lessons; they teach us, they keep us grounded and help us grow. We learn each time we fall and have to get back up. We get a different perspective and are allowed to see things from another angle. Mistakes make us stronger. They mold us into who we are and shape our personalities. We may regret a time in our life, but when you truly think back on those regrets, on those moments, you always remember the lesson they taught you.

The first time I heard the phrase, "be intentional," I was listening to a John Maxwell audiotape in the car. What exactly did "be intentional" mean? How could I "be intentional?"

If I was going to lose weight, I had to become *intentional* in my exercising. I had to become *committed* to doing something I hated. If I wanted to accomplish other tasks and projects, I had to commit myself to work on them as well. In other words, I had to become intentional.

The truth is, I already was intentional on many levels; I had just never looked at it like that. If I wanted to remember where I put my keys, I had to be intentional about where I put them when I got home (I'm terrible at this). If I wanted to remember what I walked into a room for, I had to not think of the fifty-seven other things that crossed my mind as I tried to get there. I had to be intentional about why I was walking to that room.

John Maxwell spoke on that tape about being intentional in reference to becoming successful. To reach that goal, he said, you had to be intentional in your actions, be intentional about your success and how you get there. If you want to write a book, he said, you have to carve out time each day or week and devote that time to writing your book. If you have a closet you need to be cleaned, you have to set aside time on the weekend to make it happen; we all know it's not going to clean itself.

I always tell my audiences, your career is like a ball. Nobody is going to walk up to you on your couch and give you this amazing ball. If you want the ball, you have to *take it*. Go out and grab the ball if you want it. Go out and make it happen. *Take the ball!*

Many times, I hear dental assistants say, "My boss won't send me to that course," or "They only pay for the course, and not my hourly wage while there." So? I believe you have to have some skin in the game (meaning you have to invest in yourself and take responsibility for growing). I once worked for a dentist who offered to send us to take our expanded function course. The doctor would pay for the course, but not for time, travel, food, or hotel. The doctor *did* say that we would get a raise with each course we passed. This was offered to every assistant, yet I was the *only one* who took the doctor up on it. It was the other assistants' choice not to take advantage of the offer, and yet they were resentful I had. I knew the value I was creating in myself, and I knew with knowledge comes power. They were intimated by the fact that I was willing to step out and move forward. I didn't allow them, or their fear of failure, to impact me and my growth. You will have those people in your life, please don't allow *their* fear to dictate *your* future. Negative people will drag you down, but only if you allow them to.

If your boss only pays for part of your growth, *take it*. Get some skin in the game. In this day and age, the internet makes education and growth easier than ever. There are several websites dedicated to free online education. Now there is no excuse to not educate yourself and grow. Lunch-and-learns are also a great way to get free education. Allow your sales reps to come in and give product knowledge. Learn about new services and products that will enhance you and your practice. (And hey, who doesn't love a free lunch?)

Dental assistants seldom look at themselves as leaders. Too many times we don't get the respect we deserve in our practices, and since nobody else places value on us, we don't place value on ourselves. I once worked for a wonderful doctor, but he had a tendency to talk down to me on occasion. I noticed he didn't do that to our only other team member, the front office coordinator.

I finally asked her, "Why doesn't he speak to you like he does to me?"

Her answer was, "Because I don't allow it."

That moment was an epiphany for me. I was *allowing* him to treat me like that. I had nobody to blame but myself. I only had to correct him once—not harshly; just a simple, "Please don't speak to me like that." That's all it took. He actually apologized, and that felt *great*. I was afraid of the backlash, but there was none. I had allowed my fear of being fired to override my desire to be treated better.

You are a leader in your practice. Never allow anyone to treat you like you aren't. We are creative and self-starters. We are the epitome of multitaskers, and our patients love us. They trust us. We are the backbone of the dental office. Take pride in that.

We compare ourselves to others all the time: another assistant, the hygienist, the office manager. And truly, we are in a class all our own. Many of us are formally educated; many are not. Some of us have been in this field for years and some are new to our world. We are all unique in our own right, and we need to accept that. It doesn't degrade you at all—just the opposite. Dental assisting is an amazing career. At some point, you either chose this career or it chose you (like me), but either way, use this platform to educate yourself and grow bigger and better. There are so many avenues and opportunities when you get experience. Never feel like this is a dead-end job because nothing could be farther from the truth.

TIJA'S TIDBITS

"At the end of the day, we are all accountable to ourselves- our success is a result of what we do."

CATHERINE PULSIFER

Create success with integrity. It will be success worth having.

CHAPTER 12

Navigating The Next Leg Of Your Journey

I always thought the stupidest question in a job interview was, "Where do you see yourself in five years?" To be honest, I was single and raising a little boy with no family around to help me out. I couldn't see past the end of the week let alone five years. And when you don't have a job, and no one is there to help you, you are in such a hole that I thought there was no way I could ever look that far ahead. Getting a job and providing for us at that moment at that time was what I had to focus on. How on earth could I look ahead five years?

The truth of the matter is, it's a great question. Employers want to see you have goals and are making a plan. They want to know you're going after something, not just getting by in life. What are your dreams?

I remember very distinctly riding home from the Chicago Midwinter dental education meeting in February 2010. I had attended the meeting by myself; nobody else wanted to go that year. I'm not sure exactly what it was that struck me about that year. I don't know what turned the switch on or who planted the seed. It was probably divine intervention. I knew I wanted more out of my life. I was in a bad marriage; I was very unhappy. I'm told that a little over half of the population is with their spouse or significant other for financial reasons, and I fell into that group. With my youngest son graduating in just two years, I needed to start planning my getaway. How on earth could I afford to live on my own? I mean, my paycheck was gone. There was nothing to save. So, if I took on rent and other expenses that I wasn't paying for at the time, how on earth could I manage? I needed a plan.

I pulled out a notebook that I had used to write notes in a conference session and began a list of things I wanted. I wanted to become a Certified Dental Assistant through the Dental Assistant National Boards (DANB). I wanted to write. I had loved it in school and felt I had a lot to share. I wanted to open my own dental assisting school. I didn't know how any of this was going to come to fruition; I just knew I wanted it.

I'm a big goal-setter, and I believe in writing them down. I love to go revisit goals and see what I have accomplished. Will the goals change? Of course they will. Obstacles will get in the way. Life will get in the way. But if you have no plan, then what are you reaching for? How will you know if you have gotten there if you don't know what you want?

Where are you going? I always tell my audiences I am giving them homework. They don't have to share their plan with me, but they have to make one. Make a list of all of your best qualities, then make a list of things you don't like about yourself and make those your goals to overcome. Take your bad habits, for instance. What are you willing to change to allow growth?

Many things will try to derail you, intentional or not. People will give you advice, but it's always *their* advice. Maybe it's good for them and not you. Seek advice, and lots of it, but follow your heart and do what makes you happy. Don't try to please people, because you can't. I love brussels sprouts, but if I listened to half of the people around me, I wouldn't eat them. People say they smell bad, they taste bad, and they're slimy. *Pffffft*, I say. I love my sprouts, and I will eat them with pride, no matter what people say. Sometimes, you gotta do what you gotta do, and *I will eat me some sprouts*.

A dear friend and dental icon, Linda Miles, uses this quote from former President Ronald Reagan: "Dance with the one that brung ya." It was a song from Reagan's youth, and he used it, as she does, to talk about loyalty, friendships, and support in good times and in bad. I don't believe anyone ever accomplished anything by themselves. You can't do anything without the help and support of the people in your life. If those people are negative, they will find fault with all that you do. If they are positive, you will soar.

Here are some steps to setting goals that I follow. Be diligent or follow them loosely: it doesn't matter. Just get started.

1. **What do you want to achieve?** Write down your goals and dreams and visit them often. Make short-term, easily reachable goals and make some long-term, harder goals. Celebrate each success no matter how small. Each time you succeed in reaching smaller goals, it takes you one step closer to achieving a bigger dream. It feels good to succeed, so allow yourself the time to feel good about it.

2. **Make sure the goal is something you really want.** Is the goal something

that will motivate you and make you want to go after it? Make it fun; make it something that's important to you or your family. These are the goals that will give you the most satisfaction when you achieve them. I was given the task to write a continuing education course, and I really wanted to do it. But it was *hard*. A lot of research, writing, references; it was tough. It took me way out of my comfort zone, and I had my doubts that I could pull it off. Yet I completed it, and it was published. I think I danced around for two days. The feeling I got for completing something so difficult was immense, and I celebrated that accomplishment.

3. **What is the plan? How do you get there?** When I decided on that train ride that I wanted to write an article, I had no idea what it would be about. I thought I would share my story about how I became a dental assistant. I wrote the article and allowed a friend

to read it, then another friend. Both of them gave me great suggestions, and some of them I took. Others I didn't. I wanted it to be my own. I then had to research who was going to publish this; after all, I wrote it without even knowing if anyone was going to read it. I found a wonderful publisher who not only published that article, but several more, and I continue to write for him to this day. Kevin Henry has become a dear friend, mentor, support system, shoulder, encourager, and like family. His mother and father, Ruth Ellen and Pat Henry, have become dear to me, along with his wife, Dayna. You never know who will come into your life and impact it in a positive way. This family was truly a Godsend.

4. **Stick with it.** Revisit your goals and see where you are. Did you take steps to get there? If so, what's next? If you haven't started, now is a good time. It's easy to say you want something and

then forget about it. After all, most of us will tell ourselves, "I can't do that" on a daily basis. But you can. We limit ourselves with our negative mindsets every day, but the limit to what we can accomplish doesn't exist. *Dream big.*

Looking at the big picture can be overwhelming. Break up your goals—big ones, small ones. Don't give up on a dream because you didn't make it on the first go-round. It's OK. Anything worth having is worth going after. You will make mistakes; those I call *lessons.* They will teach you what not to do the second time around. Stick with it. Life is an adventure, the journey to our dreams is half the fun.

Along the way, your goals may change. Life goes on, and maybe you will head in another direction. That's OK, too. Sometimes, getting derailed and opening our eyes to another avenue is just what we needed. Time to reset our goals. Never get discouraged. Just break up your goals into smaller pieces and go after them again with more passion and more resolve to get it done.

There is no race. Only you determine your pace. How fast or slow you go is up to you. Don't compare yourself to anyone else. Be your own person. What works for others may not work for you, so don't let someone else's journey determine your success.

TIJA'S TIDIBIT

"Stay focused, go after your dreams and keep moving toward your goals."

LL CooL J

Mistakes will happen. You will rise above them.

EPILOGUE

Step Out Of Your Comfort Zone

Getting out of your comfort zone requires
dedication, determination, and fearlessness.

I told you about my fear of writing continuing
education courses. I was terrible in school:
Spelling and grammar aren't my forte, but
then again, neither are math and science.
(I even just misspelled *grammar,* and my
computer corrected me). So, I was afraid to
take on what I saw as a monumental task.
I failed at writing several times before I
eventually got it right. I would send the piece
off, only to have the publisher write me back
and want changes. I would huff and puff,
rewrite and send it off again. I admitted to the
publisher I had no clue what I was doing, but

I learned. I have since written seven CE study courses, each one a challenge, but each one a profound accomplishment. And I *still* fail. I just get back up and do it again. I will *always* fail. It's what I do with that failure that determines my success.

It was former President Franklin D. Roosevelt, in 1933, when giving his inaugural speech who said, "The only thing we have to fear is fear itself." He went on to say, "...nameless, unreasoning, *unjustified terror* which paralyzes needed efforts to convert retreat into advance."

Our nation was in a crisis. The Great Depression had a hold on our people, and the biggest hole they dug for themselves was fear. Some had lost everything. They were afraid they would never regain their nation, their jobs, and their respect. It was a dark time in America. "Unjustified terror" is *exactly* what fear is. It cripples you. It lets doubt sneak in and makes you feel as if you are inferior. It only lives in our minds; we actually create this horrible beast inside ourselves. As we create it, so can we defeat it.

We have children come to us every day in our offices for a prophy. Some will sit and cooperate, while others won't even get in the chair. They cry, they scream; they will do *anything* to get out of there. They have no idea what this crazy person wearing pajamas, a mask, and gloves is going to do to them. They have heard the words *drill*, *pull*, and *shot*, and they want no part of it. If you can work with these kids and gain their trust, they find out there was nothing to it at all. They feared what they didn't know, and now they know, and it's not scary anymore.

The same is true for you and me. We give our fear power over us. And that fear is what tricks us into believing that we aren't good enough to accomplish great things. It holds us down and gives us every reason not to succeed. Think about what you could accomplish if you weren't afraid, if you didn't fear failing, or falling. Everything is scary until we try it—everything.

Our comfort zone is just that: comfortable.

We know everything in it. We accept it, even though we may not exactly like it. It's convenient, and we know what to expect. For years I stayed in an uncomfortable marriage. As a matter of fact, it was predictable. I knew what to expect and when to expect it. It was the *norm* for me, so I just stayed in my place. The "what if" voice kept me down and fed me negative advice: What if I fail? Where will I go? How will I make it? What if I lose everything? Eventually, I turned the what-if into a positive: What if I did make it? What if I am successful? What if everything works out? What if I am better off than I ever dreamed I would be?

Stepping out of your comfort zone means trying new things, opening your eyes to a world you're not used to. You won't like everything out there, but you will find that the outside of your comfort zone holds many secrets to success. Being in your comfort zone is all in your head. If you think you're a failure, you are. If you think you're successful, you are. Your mind and your fear is the only thing holding you back.

They say we can't achieve anything until we can actually picture ourselves in it. If you can't visualize something, chances are, you won't achieve it. If you think you can't, then you never will, but if you think you can, then nothing can stop you.

I used to be an *I-can't* person. I had no confidence, low self-esteem and, in the early years, nobody who believed in me who told me I could. I was terrible when it came to academics, so there wasn't hope for me to go to college. What was I to do? I had no direction, no desire, and no guidance. *I was a lost soul who didn't even know I was lost*. You'd have to review the chapter on my faith to realize what I did; I was being positioned to receive my gifts. I was never truly alone, and neither are you.

My journey has been one of trial and error, ups and downs. There is no magic pill or special trick I can share with you; just faith and determination mixed with hard work. We all have a story to tell, and we are no different.

I want to see you tap into your potential, to reach higher than you ever have. Whether you want to remain a dental assistant or step out of the operatory and do something else, don't let fear stop you. Write down your goals, make a plan, and plan on the plan changing, because it will. Take steps to get you where you want to be. The task will be overwhelming if you look at the big picture, so break it up, chop it up into smaller, more manageable pieces, and go after each one. Will it take time? Yes, a lot of it, but if you don't get started, it will never happen.

Always better late than never.

Life is always going to get in the way.

It may redirect you or stop you in your tracks altogether.

Pick yourself up and begin again, each time with more determination and resolve to get better.

I've heard for years that the average person changes careers five times. Where you think you want to end up may not be where you actually end up. New avenues and opportunities will come along and give you a different perspective. Be ready, because when you have a little faith and take that first step out of your comfort zone, amazing things will happen. You will grow so much, and the more you grow, the easier it is to take another step and then another. Remember, the only limits you have are those you place on yourself, so stop limiting your potential.

Another amazing thing will happen: your circle of people will grow. You'll have a bigger, stronger bond with like-minded people that will help propel you to greater things, just by the sheer fact that they believe in you and what you can accomplish. Having a support system in place is key to any success. I grew exponentially when my circle grew. I didn't have faith in myself, but the people I surround myself with to this day believe in me and encourage and empower me to take bigger leaps. I know now that my growth has no limits, and neither does yours!

Take time for yourself, write down your goals, learn all you can, and know that you can do anything you set your mind to. The people you surround yourself with are the ones who will help you get there. Don't let your environment dictate your circumstances or influence your goals. Move forward in spite of your circumstances. Work hard, but also play hard and trust in yourself. Don't compare yourself to anyone else, because they aren't you. You will forge your own path, going in the direction that's best for you.

You can do great things. You are an amazing individual. Always remember that.

TIJA'S TIDBITS

"Don't tell me I can't do something; I will prove you wrong, every time."

TIJA HUNTER

Don't allow anyone to dictate your future. This is your life. Take the ball!

APPENDIX A

Acknowledgments

Nobody gets to be successful by themselves; it truly takes a village. I want to thank so many people for helping me get to where I am today. My sons, Matthew and Brett, and their families are my guiding light and everything I do, I do for them, if for no other reason than to set an example for them to know they can do whatever they can dream. I thank my boss of fifteen years, Eric Hurtte, who supports and encourages me to learn and grow. He has pushed me to be a better me, not just for the business, but for myself. I could not be who I am today without him and the support he gives me. And to the team here at Boardwalk Family Dental, who are so amazing even when I can't be there. You work together like a well-oiled machine, and you support each other every day. You are my rockstars. To my dear Susie, you are my backbone and you keep me sane. To my very first mentor and dear friend: Linda Miles, you are an amazing source of strength and insight. You always push me to be better. To Kevin Henry, where on earth would I be without you? You have supported and encouraged me since the moment we met. You are truly an amazing friend to myself and so many. I thank you, buddy. To my first boss: Dr. Kent Splaingard, who in my first two years taught me so much about dentistry and never allowed me to give up or slack. Former coworkers like Carol and Kathy, so many laughs. To all of *my girls*, my friends who have always had my back, allowed me to cry, to laugh, and fail, picked me up and handed me a glass of wine: Jena, my soul sister, Dana and Dana, Deana, Emme, Penny, Kim, Trish and Laurie, you are all amazing and a continued source of strength. To my favorite sales rep: Cathy Hiensohn, you are amazing and your support unmatched. There are so many to name like Christian, and numerous people throughout the years that have taught me so much, I love you all!

The support that dental assistants receive from companies like Patterson Dental, Ivoclar, RevenueWell, Pro-Edge, Hu-Friedy, Henry Schein Dental, Crest Oral B, Care Credit and Air Techniques, is invaluable to our learning and growing. They see the value and worth that an assistant can bring to the dental practice and I thank you all for always supporting me and dental assistants everywhere.

Thanks to all the mistakes I've made, and there have been many, but they made me a better person.

APPENDIX B

About The Author

Tija Hunter, CDA, EFDA, CDIA, CDSO, MADAA, began her dental assisting career in 1981 and has never looked back. Being named one of the Top 25 Women in Dentistry in 2015 by *Dental Products Report* was one of the highlights of her career. She is a former vice president of the American Dental Assistants Association, where she holds the honor of Master. She has worked in her current office for fifteen years in O'Fallon, Missouri, as an office manager and dental assistant. Hunter's love of traveling takes her all over the world, where she speaks to dental assistants and dental teams.

Hunter enjoys spending time with her children and grandchildren as much as possible, and values the memories they make together.

She can be reached at; tijaefa@gmail.com or 636-487-8276, or you can find her on Facebook as Tija Bloyd Hunter.

APPENDIX C

Works Cited

Thornton, Yvonne S., and Jo Coudert. *The Ditchdigger's Daughters: A Black Family's Astonishing Success Story*. New York: Kensington, 2002.

Made in the USA
Middletown, DE
31 May 2019